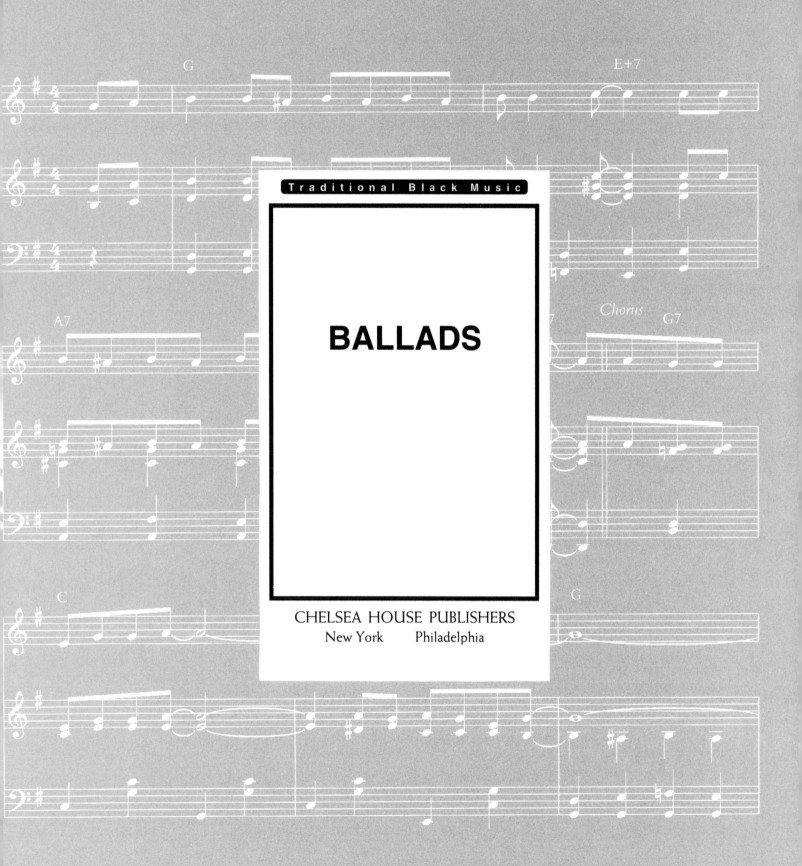

Traditional Black Music

BALLADS

CHELSEA HOUSE PUBLISHERS
New York   Philadelphia

On the Cover A musician, identified only as Happy Mose, strums his banjo in this photograph, taken around 1911. Such artists often performed songs that recounted and commented on current or past events.

Chelsea House Publishers
EDITORIAL DIRECTOR   Richard Rennert
EXECUTIVE MANAGING EDITOR   Karyn Gullen Browne
COPY CHIEF   Robin James
PICTURE EDITOR   Adrian G. Allen
CREATIVE DIRECTOR   Robert Mitchell
ART DIRECTOR   Joan Ferrigno
PRODUCTION MANAGER   Sallye Scott

Staff for Ballads
ASSISTANT EDITOR   Mary Sisson
EDITORIAL ASSISTANT   Scott D. Briggs
PICTURE RESEARCHER   Villette Harris
BOOK LAYOUT   Lydia Rivera

First Printing
1   3   5   7   9   8   6   4   2

Library of Congress Cataloging-in-Publication Data
Ballads / [compiled by] Jerry Silverman.
1 score. — (Traditional black music)
For voice and piano; includes chord symbols.
Includes index.
  ISBN 0-7910-1829-6   0-7910-1845-8 (pbk)
1. Ballads, English—United States—Juvenile. 2. Afro-Americans—
Music—Juvenile. 3. Folk music —United States—Juvenile. [1. Ballads.
2. Folk songs—United States. 3. Afro-Americans—Music.]
I. Silverman, Jerry. II. Series.
M1670.B25 1995   94-43648
                                                      CIP
                                                     AC M

Picture Credits

The Bettmann Archive: pp. 22, 57; Library of Congress: pp. 15, 32;
UPI/Bettmann: pp. 5, 12, 27, 37, 47; UPI/Bettmann Newsphotos: p. 52.

CONTENTS

Author's Preface

Everybody likes to hear a good story. And when that story is set to music, it makes the tale all the more appealing. Consequently, songs that tell stories, like ballads, exist in all societies. They may recount the heroic and epic adventures of larger-than-life protagonists or they may deal with everyday people doing everyday things. The ballads in this collection are drawn from both categories.

For a ballad to fall into the heroic-epic category it does not have to be about Greek mythology or knights errant. Milton's epic *Paradise Lost* is retold in the ballad "These Bones Gonna Rise Again," but a racehorse that wins against heavy odds ("Stewball") will do just as nicely. Other story subjects in this category include the assassination of President McKinley, an anthropomorphic insect that devastates an entire community, and a tough bird who symbolizes the indestructibility of a people. All these ballads tell grand or exaggerated stories; nevertheless, all are based on events that affected people's daily lives.

The second category of ballad deals more concretely with day-to-day events. In this category there are songs of love both true and false, including "Frankie and Johnny," "She Asked Me in the Parlor," and a trilogy of songs dealing with a particular form of lowlife—the Easy Rider. There are also work songs, soldiers' complaints, and tragic tales of death and parting.

As rich and varied as these stories are, their colorful subject matter is matched by a melodic inventiveness that gives them life. Some of the songs are designed so that everyone in the audience can join in on the chorus, while others are intended for a solo voice. There are soaring melodies and down-home blues. There are unexpected harmonies and three-chord tunes.

The joining of good stories and wonderful tunes has produced in the United States a literature of ballads that is unsurpassed anywhere. As folklorist B. A. Botkin states: "Almost every phase or period of American life has left its record in the form of folk songs that describe, reflect, or evoke the time and the place, their conditions, customs, and characters. In this sense American folk song provides . . . a history of, by, and for the people, in which for the first time the people speak and are allowed to tell their own story, in their own way."

Jerry Silverman

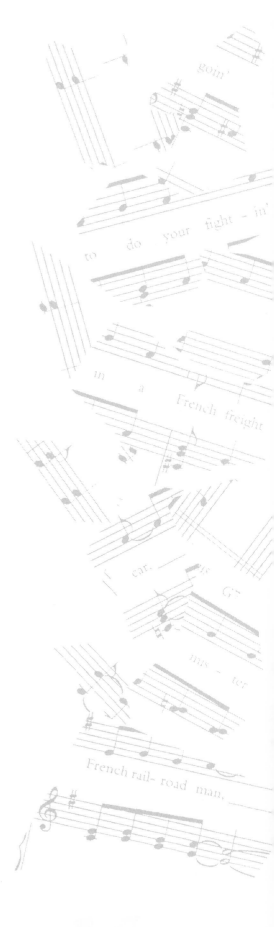

The Contribution of Blacks to American Art and Culture

Kenneth B. Clark

Historical and contemporary social inequalities have obscured the major contribution of American blacks to American culture. The historical reality of slavery and the combined racial isolation, segregation, and sustained educational inferiority have had deleterious effects. As related pervasive social problems determine and influence the art that any group can not only experience but also, ironically, the extent to which they can eventually contribute to the society as a whole, this tenet is even more visible when assessing the contributions made by African Americans.

All aspects of the arts have been pursued by black Americans, but music provides a special insight into the persistent and inescapable social forces to which black Americans have been subjected. One can speculate that in their preslavery patterns of life in Africa, blacks used rhythm, melody, and lyrics to hold on to reality, hope, and the acceptance of life. Later, in America, music helped blacks endure the cruelties of slavery. Spirituals and gospel music provided a medium for both communion and communication. As the black experience in America became more complex, so too did black music, which has grown and ramified, dramatically affecting the development of American music in general. The result is that today, more than ever before, black music provides a powerful lens through which we may view the history of black Americans in a new and revealing way.

Celebrated blues singer, musician, and composer Big Bill Broonzy recorded and popularized several blues ballads during his career.

The most famous horse race in folk music history took place in Kildare, Ireland, in the late 18th or early 19th century. The race matched Miss Portly, a gray mare, with Sku-Ball, a skewbald horse (a horse with brown and white patches on its coat), who won the race in an upset. The event was commemorated in an Irish street ballad that first appeared in print in the United States as "Skewball" in 1829. At some point the ballad was learned by slaves, who completely overhauled the music, story, and locale. All that remains of the original in this song is a variant of the horse's name (Stewball) and the incident of the race itself.

STEWBALL

long, long, long, __ See her tra - vel all day long, all day long.

Well, I don't mind horse racing
If it wasn't for my wife.
Old Stewball may stumble,
And away with my life, wife and baby.
Left behind, wife and baby,
Left behind, left behind.

Old Stewball was a black horse,
Just as slick as a mole.
He had a ring 'round his fore-shoulder
And it shined just like gold.
Like gold, like gold,
And it shined just like gold.

Old Stewball was a racehorse,
But the poor horse was blind;
He ran so fast down in Texas,
He left his shadow behind.
Behind, behind,
He left his shadow behind.

Old Stewball was a racehorse,
And old Molly, she was too;
Old Molly, she stumbled
And Old Stewball flew 'round the track
All day long, 'round the race-track,
All day long, all day long.

Elizabeth Cotton was a left-handed guitarist who sang ballads and blues for many years in the household of the Seeger family, where she was employed as a maid. The Seegers—musicologist Charles, his composer wife, Ruth, and their children Mike and Peggy (who were later to make their mark in the folksinging world along with their elder half brother, Pete)—recognized "Libba" Cotton's importance as a true folk original. Her unique guitar style and her inexhaustible repertoire inspired and enchanted legions of players and singers. She went on to record many of her songs and to appear at numerous folk music concerts and festivals in the 1960s and 1970s. "O Babe, It Ain't No Lie" was one of the songs she performed.

O BABE, IT AIN'T NO LIE

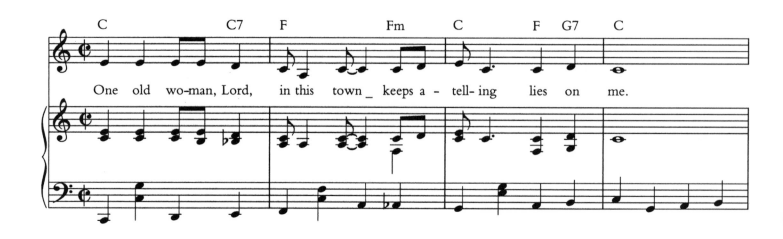

One old wo-man, Lord, in this town keeps a-tell-ing lies on me.

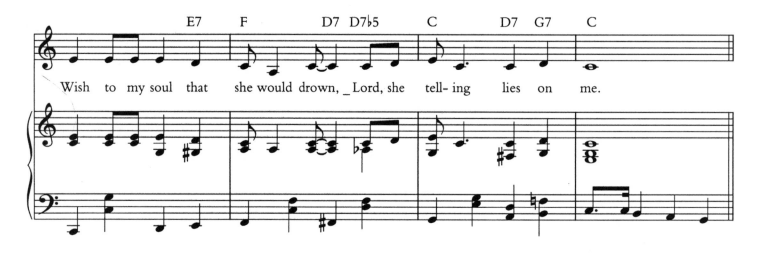

Wish to my soul that she would drown, Lord, she tell-ing lies on me.

Chorus

O, babe, it ain't no lie.

8

Been all around this whole round world,
Lord, and I just got back today.
Work all the week, honey, and I give it all to you,
Honey baby, what more can I do?

9

On September 6, 1901, President William McKinley was shot while attending the Pan-American Exposition in Buffalo, New York. After White House officials had announced that McKinley was doing well and would survive, he collapsed and died on September 14. His assassin, a young anarchist named Leon Czolgosz, was seized on the spot and was tried, convicted, and executed in less than a month. Upon McKinley's death Theodore Roosevelt assumed the presidency. This fanciful ballad appeared shortly after the assassination. Although it originated among white singers, it was quickly adopted by black blues singers.

WHITE HOUSE BLUES

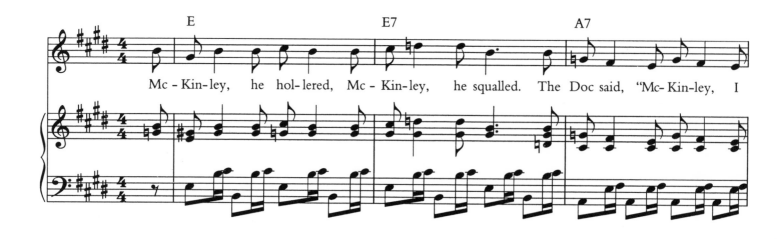

Oh it's look here you rascal, see what you done,
You shot my husband and I got your gun,
I'm takin' you back to Washington.

Oh the doc come a-running, took off his specs,
Said, "Mr. McKinley, better cash in your checks,
You're bound to die, bound to die."

Oh Roosevelt in the White House doin' his best,
McKinley in the graveyard takin' a rest,
He's gone, long gone.

The engine she whistled all down the line,
Blown' at every station, "McKinley is dyin',"
From Buffalo to Washington.

Roosevelt in the White House, drinkin' out a silver cup,
McKinley in the graveyard, he'll never wake up,
He's gone a long, old time.

This song, like "Stewball," is an 18th-century Irish ballad that crossed the Atlantic and was adapted by black singers. It was first published in an Irish broadside as "The Unfortunate Rake" around 1790. "The Unfortunate Rake" told the sad tale of a soldier visiting a military hospital where he finds a comrade-in-arms dying of what is apparently syphilis. The moribund young man requests an elaborate military funeral with a band and an escort of "six young harlots." Similar dying wishes occur not only in "St. James Infirmary" (where the military band has become a jazz band and the harlots have been toned down to "pretty girls"), but also in the cowboy ballad "The Streets of Laredo" (where the requests are made by a cowboy who has been shot in a "card-house").

St. James Infirmary

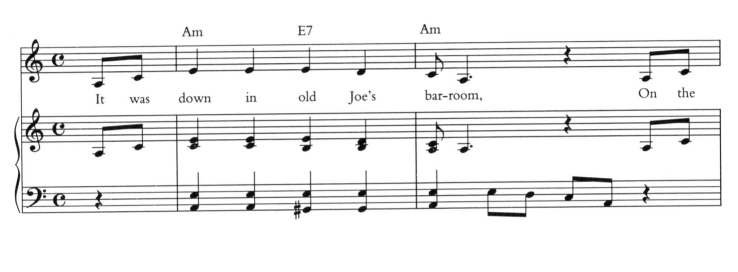

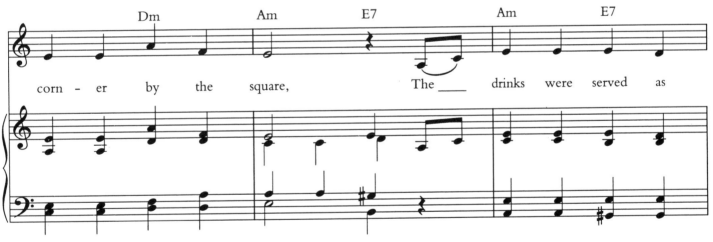

On my left stood big Joe McKennedy,
His eyes were bloodshot red.
He turned to the crowd around him,
These were the very words he said.

"I went down to the St. James Infirmary
To see my baby there.
She was stretched out on a long white table,
So pale, so cold and so fair."

Let her go, let her go, God-bless her,
Wherever she may be.
She may search this whole world over,
Never find a man as sweet as me.

When I die, please bury me
In my high-top Stetson hat.
Put a twenty-dollar gold piece on my watch chain,
So the gang'll know I died standing pat.

I want six crap shooters for pall bearers.
Six pretty gals to sing me a song.
Put a jazz band on my hearse wagon
To raise hell as we stroll along.

And now that you've heard my story,
I'll have another shot of booze.
And if anybody happens to ask you,
I've got the St. James Infirmary blues."

A wounded World War I veteran greets a spectator at a parade held in New York City in March 1919. The experiences and stories of such soldiers made their way into a number of popular ballads.

The little boll weevil, which reportedly could eat its way across 40 miles of cotton fields a year, nearly destroyed the land of King Cotton. This voracious insect prefers to do its feasting and lay its eggs in the tender unopened cotton boll, known as the square. The boll weevil first infested the United States in 1892, spreading quickly from Texas to Louisiana, Arkansas, Mississippi, Alabama, Georgia, and South Carolina.

THE BOLL WEEVIL

Oh, the boll weev-il is a lit-tle black bug, Come from Mex - i - co, they say. Come

all the way to Tex - as, Just a - look-in' for a place to stay. Just a- look-in' for a

home, _____ Just a- look-in' for a home. _____ Just a- look-in' for a

The first time I seen the boll weevil,
He was sitting on the square.
The next time I seen the boll weevil,
He had all his family there,
Just a-lookin' for a home.   (2)

The farmer said to the weevil,
"What makes your face so red?"
The weevil said to the farmer,
"It's a wonder I ain't dead,"
Just a-lookin' for a home.   (2)

The farmer took the boll weevil,
And he put him in hot sand.
The weevil said, "This is mighty hot,
But I'll stand it like a man.
This'll be my home, this'll be my home."   (2)

The farmer took the boll weevil,
And he put him in a lump of ice
The boll weevil said to the farmer,
"This is mighty cold and nice.
This'll be my home."   (2)

The farmer took the boll weevil,
And he put him in the fire.
The boll weevil said to the farmer,
"This is just what I desire.
This'll be my home."   (2)

The boll weevil said to the farmer,
"You better leave me alone;
I ate up all your cotton,
And I'm starting on your corn,
I'll have a home, I'll have a home."   (2)

The merchant got half the cotton,
The boll weevil for the rest.
Didn't leave the farmer's wife
But one old cotton dress,
And it's full of holes, and it's full of holes.   (2)

The farmer said to the merchant,
"We're in an awful fix;
The boll weevil ate all the cotton up
And left us only sticks,
We got no home, we got no home."   (2)

The farmer said to the merchant,
"We ain't made but one bale,
And before we'll give you that one,
We'll fight and go to jail,
We'll have a home, we'll have a home."   (2)

And if anybody should ask you
Who was it sang this song,
It was it the poor old farmer
With all but his blue jeans gone,
A-looking for a home.   (2)

This photograph, taken in 1887, shows black workers picking cotton in a Georgia field. A few years later, the boll weevil would devastate the productive cotton fields of the South.

Woah, the hardest battle was ever on the western plains,
When me and a bunch o' cowboys ran into Jesse James.

So sings the great twelve-string guitarist Leadbelly in his song "When I Was a Cowboy." "I Went Down to the Depot" is a longer, if somewhat vague, account of the exploits and death of James, who was using the alias Howard when he was shot in the back by a fellow outlaw. According to the April 3, 1882, *Saint Joseph Evening News* of Missouri, "Between eight and nine o'clock yesterday morning Jesse James, the Missouri outlaw . . . was instantly killed by . . . Robert Ford . . . in this city . . . who had the courage to draw on the notorious outlaw even when his back was turned."

I WENT DOWN TO THE DEPOT

Chorus

Poor Jes - se James, poor Jes - se James, I'll ne - ver see my Jes - se an - y more; _ 'Twas a dir - ty lit - tle cow - ard, He shot Mis - ter How - ard, And he laid Jes - se James in his grave.

Jesse James was a man and he had a robber band,
And he flagged down the east bound train.
   Robert Ford watched his eye,
   And he shot him on the sly,
And they laid Jesse James in his grave. *Chorus*

Jesse James' little wife was a moaner all her life
When they laid Jesse James in his grave.
   She earned her daily bread
   By her needle and her thread
When they laid Jesse James in his grave. *Chorus*

Last chorus: Poor Jesse James, poor Jesse James,
           I'll never see my Jesse any more.
           Robert Ford's pistol ball
           Brought him tumbling from the wall
           And laid Jesse James in his grave.

"Poor Howard" gives no clues as to who Howard was or how he came to be "dead and gone." But the name Howard (as opposed to names like Jim, Bill, and John) is uncommon enough in folk songs to open the possibility that Howard is the famous "Mr. Howard" of the preceding song—namely, the notorious Jesse James. James's fame and mystique captured the popular imagination and inspired a number of artists and singers.

POOR HOWARD

Poor How - ard's dead and gone, Left me here to sing this song,

Poor How - ard's dead and gone, Left me here to sing this song.

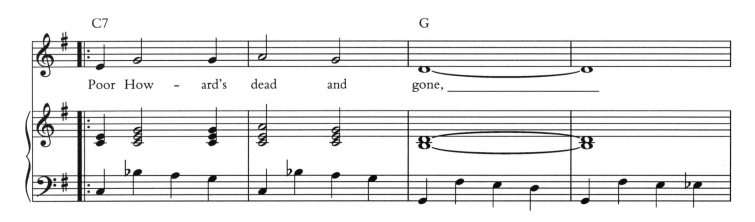

Poor How - ard's dead and gone, _____

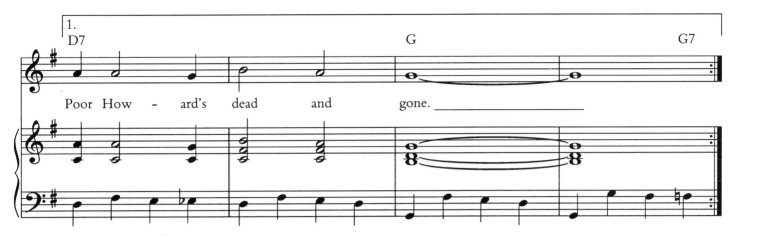

1.
D7   G   G7

Poor How - ard's dead   and   gone. _____

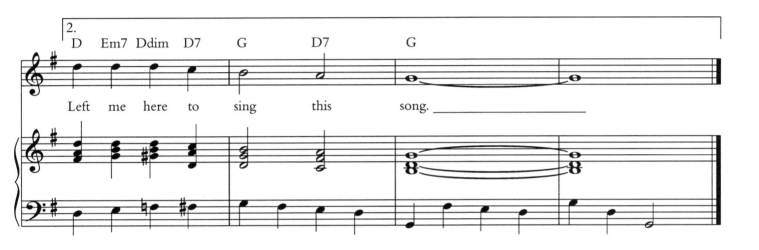

2.
D Em7 Ddim D7   G   D7   G

Left me here to sing this   song. _____

Who's been here since I've been gone?
Pretty little girl with a red dress on.
Who's been here since I've been gone?
Pretty little girl with a red dress on.
Pretty little girl with a red dress on,
Pretty little girl with a red dress on,
Pretty little girl with a red dress on,
Left me here to sing this song.

Who's been here since I've been gone?
Great big man with a derby on.
Who's been here since I've been gone?
Great big man with a derby on.
Great big man with a derby on,
Great big man with a derby on,
Great big man with a derby on,
Left me here to sing this song.

Jack Johnson want to get on board,
Captain said, "I ain't haulin' no coal."
Cryin', fare thee, Titanic, fare thee well.

The sinking of the "unsinkable" ocean liner *Titanic* on its maiden voyage has inspired many a ballad, including Leadbelly's sardonic comment on the refusal of the White Star shipping company to allow black heavyweight boxing champion Jack Johnson to book passage on their ill-fated ship. The *Titanic* sank on the night of April 14–15, 1912, and has been the subject of songs ever since, including one that contains the chorus "It was sad when that great ship went down," sung to an incongruously rousing and cheerful tune. "The Titanic" evokes a grimmer mood with its sudden modulation into minor mode.

THE TITANIC

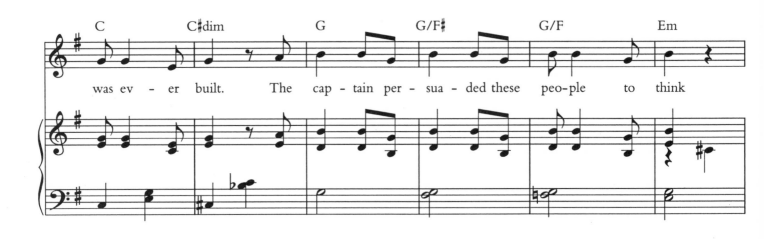

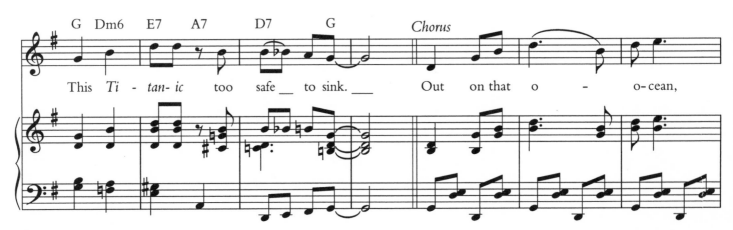

The great wide o - o-cean, The Ti -

tan - ic out on the o - cean, Sink-in' down. _____

The ship left the harbor at a rapid speed,
'Twuz carrying everything that the peoples need.
She sailed six-hundred miles that day,
Met an iceberg in her way.   *Chorus*

The ship left the harbor, 'twuz running fast.
'Twuz her first trip and her last.
Way out on that ocean wide,
An iceberg ripped her in the side.   *Chorus*

Up come Bill from the bottom floor,
Said the water was running in the boiler door.
Go back, Bill, and shut your mouth,
Got forty-eight pumps to keep the water out!   *Chorus*

Just about then the captain looked around,
He seen the *Titanic* was a-sinking down.
He give orders to the men around:
"Get your life-boats and let 'em down!"   *Chorus*

The men standing 'round like heroes brave,
Nothing but the women and the children to save.
The women and children a-wiping their eyes,
Kissing their husbands and friends good-bye.   *Chorus*

On the fifteenth of April in nineteen-twelve,
The ship sank down in the ocean swell.
The people was thinking of Jesus o' Nazarree,
While the band played "Nearer, My God, To Thee!"   *Chorus*

Champion boxer Jack Johnson and his wife ride a more fortunate ship than the
Titanic. Johnson was an exceptional boxer who won 107 of his 114 career fights,
but he had to flee the United States in 1913 for violating the Mann Act, which forbade
interracial sexual relations.

22

This prison camp work song was recorded by Pete Seeger on March 12, 1951, at the Retrieve State Farm in Angleton, Texas, some 50 miles south of Houston. It is a work chant performed in call-and-response style, with a heavy emphasis on the rhythm. The grizzly bear in the song is an allegorical beast who stands for all the hardships that the convicts must endure, from the shotgun-toting captain who supervises the work crew to the daily degradation of the Jim Crow South.

GRIZZLY BEAR

He had great long tushes like a grizzly bear.   (2)

He made a track in the bottom like a grizzly bear.   (2)

Tell me, who was the grizzly, grizzly bear.   (2)

Jack o' Diamonds was the grizzly, grizzly bear.   (2)

He made a noise in the bottom like a grizzly bear.   (2)

Well, my mama was scared of that grizzly bear.   (2)

Well, my papa went a-hunting for the grizzly bear.   (2)

Well, my brother wasn't scared of that grizzly bear.   (2)

Well, I'm a-gonna get that grizzly bear.   (2)

No matter what people do to the gray goose, he survives. The family shoots
him, plucks him, and boils him, all to no avail. Knife and fork make no impression;
he is tougher than the hogs' jawbones and impervious to the buzz saw. Like the
grizzly bear, the gray goose is a larger-than-life symbolic animal. But while the
bear symbolizes oppression, the goose stands for defiance and survival. Leadbelly
recalled singing this song with the other convicts in a Texas prison to express their
contempt for their white jailers and their admiration for prisoners who stood up to
the jailers' cruelties.

THE GRAY GOOSE

My daddy went a-huntin' . . .
He was huntin' for the gray goose . . .

And he went to the big wood . . .
And he took along his shotgun . . .

Along come a gray goose . . .
Well, he up to his shoulder . . .

And he rammed back the hammer . . .
And he pulled on the trigger . . .

And the shotgun went "boo-loo". . .
And the shotgun went "boo-loo". . .

Down he come a-fallin' . . .
He was six weeks a-fallin' . . .

And he put him on the wagon . . .
And he took him to the white house . . .

And your wife and my wife . . .
They give a feather-pickin' . . .

They were six weeks a-pickin' . . .
They were six weeks a-pickin' . . .

And they put him on a parboil . . .
He was six weeks a-parboil . . .

And they put him on the table . . .
And they put him on the table . . .

And the fork couldn't stick him . . .
And the knife couldn't prick him . . .

Well, they throwed him in the hogpen . . .
And the hogs couldn't eat him . . .

Well, he broke the sow's jawbone . . .
Well, he broke the sow's jawbone . . .

So they took him to the sawmill . . .
And he broke the saw's teeth out . . .

And the last time I seen him . . .
And the last time I seen him . . .

He was flyin' 'cross the ocean . . .
Had a long string of goslins . . .

And they all went "Quonk, quonk". . .
And they all went "Quonk, quonk". . .

The story of Frankie, who guns down her faithless man, Johnny, appears with
varying details in an astonishing number of songs, making it perhaps the most
celebrated case of domestic violence in American history. The poet Carl Sandburg,
who claimed to be familiar with over a hundred versions of the song, said, "A Frankie
song is like a grand opera role; interpretations vary. . . . If America has a classical
gutter song, it is the one that tells of Frankie and her man."

FRANKIE AND JOHNNY

Frank-ie and John - ny were sweet hearts. _ Oh Lord- y, how __ they could

love. Swore to be true ___ to each oth - er, ___

Frankie and Johnny went walking, Johnny in his brand new suit.
"Oh, good Lord," said Frankie, "Don't my Johnny man look cute?" *Chorus*

Johnny said, "I've got to leave you, but I won't be very long,
Don't wait up for me, honey, or worry while I'm gone." *Chorus*

Frankie went down to the corner to get a bucket of beer.
She said to the fat bartender, "Has my lovin' man been here?" *Chorus*

"Well, I ain't gonna tell you no story, I ain't gonna tell you no lie,
I saw your Johnny 'bout an hour ago with a gal named Nellie Bly." *Chorus*

Frankie pulled out her six-shooter, pulled out her old forty-four.
Her gun went rooty-toot-toot-toot, and Johnny rolled over the floor. *Chorus*

"Oh, roll me over so easy; oh, roll me over so slow,
Oh, roll me over easy, boys, for my wounds, they hurt me so." *Chorus*

Frankie got down on her knees, took Johnny into her lap.
She started to hug and to kiss him, but there was no bringing him back. *Chorus*

"Oh, get me a thousand policemen, and throw me into your cell,
'Cause I've shot my Johnny so dead, I know I'm going to hell." *Chorus*

Roll out your rubber-tired carriage. Roll out your old-time hack.
There's twelve men going to the graveyard and eleven coming back. *Chorus*

The judge said to the jury, "It's plain as plain can be;
This woman shot her lover, it's murder in the second degree." *Chorus*

Now, it was not murder in the second degree, and it was not murder in the third,
The woman simply dropped her man, like a hunter drops a bird. *Chorus*

Frankie mounted to the scaffold as calm as a girl can be,
And turning her eyes to heaven, she said, "Nearer, my God, to Thee." *Chorus*

Now, this story has no moral— this story has no end.
But a man's the cause of all trouble ever since the world began. *Chorus*

*Couples dance in a lively Harlem, New York, nightclub. The spirited nightlife of Harlem
has inspired many a ballad.*

Of man's first disobedience, and the fruit
Of that forbidden tree whose mortal taste
Brought death into the World, and all our woe,
With loss of Eden, till one greater Man
Restore us and regain the blissful seat . . .

So run the opening lines of John Milton's *Paradise Lost*. The epic tale of man's fall from grace has been told and retold through the ages, but nowhere has it been recounted with the syncopated bounce found in "These Bones Gonna Rise Again."

THESE BONES GONNA RISE AGAIN

"Adam, Adam, where art thou?"
These bones gonna rise again.
"Here, Marse Lord, I'm coming down."
These bones gonna rise again. *Chorus*

Similarly

Thought he'd make a woman too . . .
Didn't know 'xactly what to do . . . *Chorus*

Took a rib from Adam's side . . .
Made Miss Eve for to be his bride . . . *Chorus*

Put 'em in a garden rich and fair . . .
Told 'em to eat what they found there . . . *Chorus*

To one tall tree they must not go . . .
There must the fruit forever grow . . . *Chorus*

Old Miss Eve come a-walking 'round . . .
Spied that tree all loaded down . . . *Chorus*

Sarpent he came 'round the trunk . . .
At Miss Eve his eye he wunk . . . *Chorus*

First she took a little pull . . .
Then she filled her apron full . . . *Chorus*

Adam he come prowling 'round . . .
Spied them peelings on the ground . . . *Chorus*

Then he took a little slice . . .
Smack his lips and said 'twas nice . . . *Chorus*

Lord he spoke with a mighty voice . . .
Shook the heavens to the joists . . . *Chorus*

"Adam, Adam, where art thou?" . . .
"Yes, Marse Lord, I'm a-coming now." . . . *Chorus*

"You et my apples, I believe?" . . .
"Not me, Lord, but I 'spec' 'twas Eve." . . . *Chorus*

Lord then rose up in his wrath . . .
Told 'em beat it down the path . . . *Chorus*

"Out of my garden you must git." . . .
"For you and me has got to quit." . . . *Chorus*

For a young man to be "asked in the parlor" was serious business in 19th-century America. The parlor was where declarations of love were made and where parents either consented or refused to give their daughter's hand in marriage to dark-eyed (and other) hopefuls. This song is like a three-act drama: in the first verse, there is an avowal of love; in the second, the parents reject the suitor; and in the third, the happy couple marries. Obviously, not every invitation to the parlor had such fortunate results.

SHE ASKED ME IN THE PARLOR

Well, she asked me in her par-lor, An' she cooled me with her fan,

An' she whis-pered to her moth-er, "O Ma, I love that dark-eyed man."

Well, I ask her mother for her
An' she said she was too young.
Lawd, I wished I never had seen her
An' I wished she'd never been born.

Well, I led her to de altar,
An' de preacher give his comman',
An' she swore by God that made her
That she never love another man.

There are few images in traditional American song more poignant than the "lonesome road." It appears in many similar songs dealing with love, prison, separation, and death. On the one hand, the image of the road creates the mournful feeling of rootlessness that accompanies the frequent journeys and moves that are a part of American life; on the other hand, it is also a symbol of opportunity, the chance to leave a troubled place for a better life elsewhere.

GOIN' DOWN THAT LONESOME ROAD

Goin' down that lone-some road, O, goin' down that lone-some road, An' I

won't be treat-ed this-a way. Springs on my bed done

brok - en down, An' I ain't got no-where to lay my head.

Lost my mama and my papa, too,   (2)
And it left me all alone with you.
You cause me to weep and cause me to moan,
And you cause me to leave my happy home.   *Chorus*

Longest train I ever saw   (2)
It was nineteen coaches long.
What makes you grieve me night and day?
And I won't be treated this-a-way.   *Chorus*

Homeless blacks gather with their belongings along a bleak stretch of road. Ballads such as "Going down That Lonesome Road" capture the spirit of the journeys and migrations that are part of American history.

"Look Down That Lonesome Road" is an excellent example of a mournful "lonesome road" song. It has a slow, rocking, blueslike melody with a heartbreaking harmonic shift in the second measure. It tells a woeful tale of irrevocable parting. The line "hang down your head and sigh," is reminiscent of the earlier spirituals, with their emphasis on the misery and despair to be found on earth.

LOOK DOWN THAT LONESOME ROAD

True love, true love, what have I done,
That you should treat me so?
You caused me to talk and to walk
Like I never done before.

I wish to God that I had died,
Had died 'fore I was born.
Before I seen your smilin' face,
And heard your lyin' tongue.

My old Jerry is an Arkansas mule,
Been everywhere and he ain't no fool.
Work is heavy, old Jerry get sore;
Pull so much and won't pull no more.

Paul Bunyan had his great blue ox, Babe. The cowboy had his faithful pony. Jerry the mule was the tireless companion of the sharecropper. Stubborn and tough, he and the poor farmer were bound together for life. This song's sixth and seventh verses tell the traditional tale of Mike and Jerry, two mules who broke loose from their driver and ran from "Jerome" (which may be a corruption of the town name of Rome) to Decatur, Georgia—a distance of about 100 miles—in a single day. Alternately, "Mike an' Jerry" may be a corruption of "Hikin' Jerry," in which case only one mule would have made the journey.

I GOT A MULEY

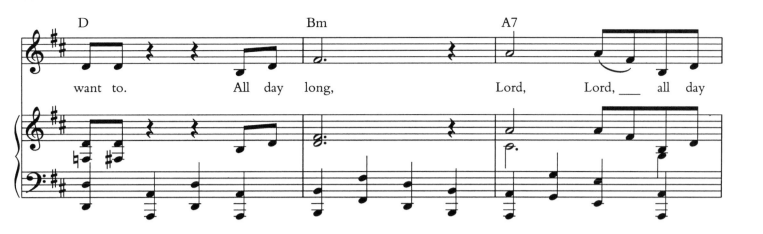

want to.   All day long,   Lord,   Lord,___ all day

long.   Lord, this old   by.

Lawd, thin ol' mountain,
Mountain must be hanted,⎬ (2)
My light goes out,
Lawd, Lawd, my light goes out.

I'm gonna buy me,
Buy me a magnified lantern.⎬ (2)
'Twon't go out,
Lawd, Lawd, won't go out.

I'm gonna buy me,
Buy me a Winchester rifle,⎬ (2)
Box o' balls,
Lawd, Lawd, box o' balls.

I gonna back my,
Back myself in the mountains⎬ (2)
To play bad,
Lawd, Lawd, to play bad.

Mike an' Jerry
Must be a gasoline burner;⎬ (2)
Didn't stop here,
Lawd, Lawd, didn't stop here.

Mike an' Jerry
Hiked from Jerome to Decatur⎬ (2)
In one day,
Lawd, Lawd, in one day.

This work song was sung to the accompaniment of swinging pickaxes. It was first published in the 1920s in the groundbreaking publication, *Negro Workaday Songs*, by Howard Odum and Guy Johnson, who heard it near Chapel Hill, North Carolina. The "walker" in this song is the overseer of the job, who was sometimes called the "walking boss." The song expresses the singer's hope that he can work on the job as long as he wishes and then quit without any harassment from the walker.

I DON'T WANT NO TROUBLE
WITH THE WALKER

Oh, me an' my buddy
Jes' came here this mornin'. } (2)
Wanta go home,
Lawd, Lawd, wanta go home.

I can drive it,
Drive it long as anybody, } (2)
Wanta go home,
Lawd, Lawd, wanta go home.

Cap'n, did you hear about,
Hear about two your womens gonna leave you? } (2)
Wanta go home,
Lawd, Lawd, wanta go home.

I'm gonna roll here,
Roll here a few days longer, } (2)
I'm goin' home,
Lawd, Lawd, I'm goin' home.

Prison laborers carry sandbags to reinforce a levee. Groups of laborers were usually overseen by a "walker," who was often free to abuse or harass the workers.

This song was a combination work and party song. On the weekend it was played at dances and other social get-togethers; during the week it was sung (usually in a low undertone) to get through the hours of tedious manual labor most blacks had to perform. It is similar to "Grizzly Bear" in its use of animals to symbolize oppression, while its loose structure resembles "Shot My Pistol in the Heart of Town" and "In the Pines."

SHOOT THAT BUFFALO

Went down to Ra - leigh, Was nev - er there be - fore,

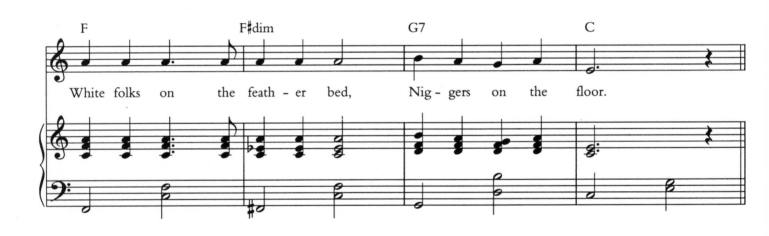

White folks on the feath - er bed, Nig - gers on the floor.

Shoot that buf - fa, shoot that lo, Shoot that buf - fa - lo.

Went down to low groun'
To gather up my corn,
Raccoon sot the dogs on me,
'Possum blowed his horn.

Las' year was a bad crop year,
Ev'ybody knowed it.
I didn't make but a bushel o' corn
An' some damn rascal stoled it.

I had ol' back-band,
It was made out o' leather;
Kept me all the doggone time
Keepin' it sewed together.

An "easy rider" is an unpleasant character who lives—and lives well—off the efforts of his woman or women. Jazz pianist Jelly Roll Morton, reminiscing about his youth in the tenderloin district of New Orleans during the early 1900s, had this to say about some easy riders he had known: "The chippies in their little-girl dresses were standing in the crib doors singing the blues. Then you could observe the fancy Dans, dressed fit to kill, wearing their big diamonds—sports like Willie the Pleaser . . . Chinee Morris . . . Okey Poke . . . Ed Mochez (who left a hundred and ten suits when he died). . . . These guys were all big gamblers, and had all the best women and a lot of them smoked hop or used coke."

EASY RIDER

made me love you, now your gal has come.

Well, it's hey, hey, hey, hey, hey.

1.

Final ending

If I was a catfish, swimmin' in the deep blue sea,
If I was a catfish, swimmin' in the deep blue sea,
I would swim across the ocean, bring my baby back to me.
Well, it's hey, hey, hey, hey, hey.

I'm goin' away, Rider, and I won't be back till fall,
I'm goin' away, Rider, and I won't be back till fall,
And if I find me a good man, I won't be back at all.
Well, it's hey, hey, hey, hey, hey.

This rider song is sometimes called "See See Rider." As a child, the legendary Big Bill Broonzy knew a wandering musician named See See Rider, but he was named after the song (one of his favorites), not vice versa. Young Broonzy examined Rider's homemade musical instruments until he figured out how to build them himself. When he saw Broonzy's instruments, Rider realized that the boy seriously wanted to be a musician, and he did the world of music an immense favor by teaching Broonzy how to play.

C.C. RIDER

now _____ your wo-man's come.　　　　　　　　　　　　　You

You caused me, Rider, to hang my head and cry,
You put me down; God knows I don't see why.
You put me down; God knows I don't see why.
You put me down; God knows I don't see why.

If I had a headlight like on a passenger train,
I'd shine my light on cool Colorado Springs.
I'd shine my light on cool Colorado Springs.
I'd shine my light on cool Colorado Springs.

That Sunshine Special comin' 'round the bend,
It blowed just like it never blowed before.
It blowed just like it never blowed before.
It blowed just like it never blowed before.

Yet another look at the uneasy relationship between the rider and his woman—but with a difference. In this song she has the guts to stand up to her rider, telling him that either he shapes up or she ships out. Despite the woman's strength and self-respect, this song is not what would be considered a feminist statement nowadays. The rider's woman plans to return to her "used-to-be rider," and she anticipates being troubled by the blues once she leaves her current rider.

I Know You Rider

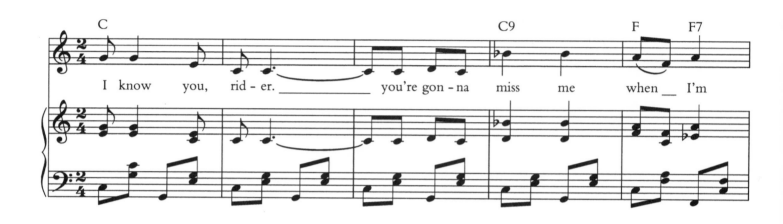

I know you, rid-er. _____ you're gon-na miss me when __ I'm

gone, _____ I know you, rid-er. _____ you're gon-na

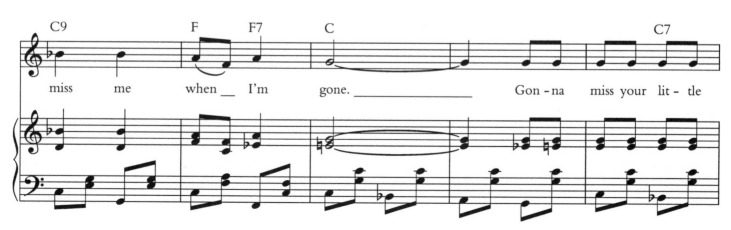

miss me when __ I'm gone. _____ Gon-na miss your lit-tle

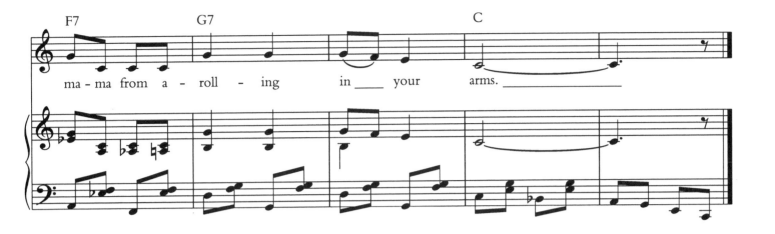

ma - ma from a - roll - ing in ___ your arms. _____

I'm goin' down the road where I can get more decent care, (2)
Goin' back to my used-to-be rider 'cause I don't feel welcome here.

I'm goin' down to the river, set in my rocking chair, (2)
And if the blues don't find me, gonna rock away from here.

I know my baby sure is bound to love me some, (2)
'Cause he throws his arms around me like a circle 'round the sun.

Lovin' you baby, just as easy as rollin' off a log, (2)
But if I can't be your woman, I sure ain't gonna be your dog.

I laid down last night tryin' to take a rest. (2)
But my mind kept rambling like the wild geese in the West.

Sun gonna shine in my back yard some day, (2)
And the wind gonna rise up, baby, blow my blues away.

The word "careless" in this song means uncaring rather than the opposite of careful. Here is the oft-told tale of the "false true lover," the smooth talker who leads the unsuspecting maiden astray then deserts and denies her when she becomes pregnant. While the subject is as old as the hills, the music is that of the blues. The thrice-repeated lines make this song perfect for group singing.

CARELESS LOVE

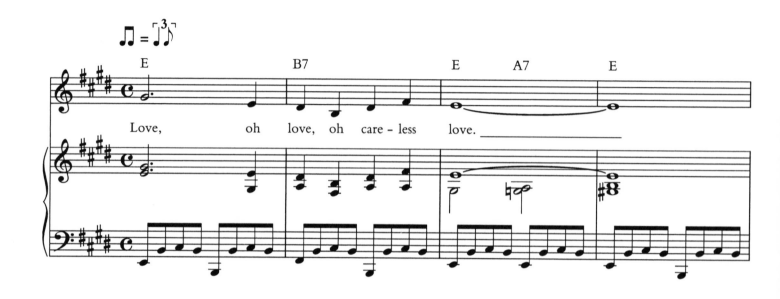

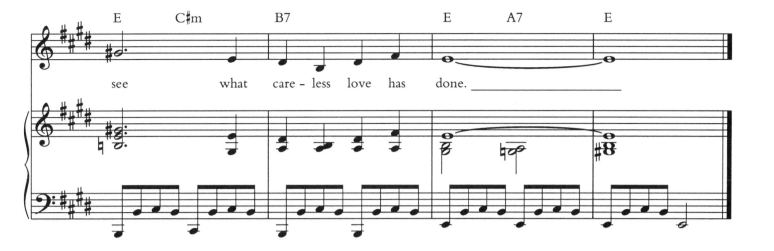

see — what care-less love has done. _____

I cried last night and the night before, (3)
Gonna cry tonight and cry no more.

I love my momma and my poppa too, (3)
But I'd leave them both to go with you.

When I wore an apron low, (3)
You'd follow me through rain and snow.

Now I wear my apron high, (3)
You see my door and pass on by.

How I wish that train would come, (3)
And take me back where I come from.

An amateur blues singer wows musician Nat Williams with her talent. Many blues songs rely for their subject matter on the old staple of betrayed or unrequited love.

This is the somewhat confused story of a man who is in deep trouble. He fires his gun, has an altercation with the authorities, and scares women—all somehow linked to a card game. Songs that tell stories about bad men are fairly common in black folk music; others include "Outrun That Cop" and "I Steal That Corn." While some songs are judgmental and disapproving, others are sympathetic or humorous, filled with details of wild exploits that are more entertaining than criminal.

Shot my Pistol in the Heart of Town

Very freely

O Lawd,
Which a-way
Did the po' gal go?
She lef' here runnin',
Is all I know.

O Lawd,
Which a-way
Do the Red River run?
Lawd, it run east and west
Like the risin' sun.

O Lawd,
Black gal hollered,
Like to scared my brown to death.
If I hadn't had my pistol
I'd a-run myself.

O Lawd,
Jes' two cards
In the deck I love
Lawd, the Jack o' Diamonds
An' the Ace o' Clubs.

O Lawd,
Stopped here to play
Jes' one mo' game.
Lawd, Jack o' Diamonds
Petered on my han'.

This song dates from World War I. It was collected by Lieutenant John Jacob Niles, an American aviator who became a singer and compiler of folk songs. In his 1927 book, *Singing Soldiers*, Niles explains the word "Bush" in the chorus of the song by relating the following yarn, told to him by a soldier who had served on the front lines: "Now boy, dis here French army is a whale of a fightin' machine. . . . Dey has all de trick affairs for makin' war . . . long range guns, grenades, and a passel of inventions we ain't never heard of yit. . . . Yes, and dese English lads—wonderful fighters. . . . Dey drinks a lot of tea but dey does fight. . . . An' de Italians, *an'* de Austrians, *an'* de Belgians, *an'* de Germans wid dose machine guns dat shoot so slow and go in so deep. But Mister, let me tell you dis one thing. . . . If ever you have to go out yonder and have to fight in dis war like I did . . . take my word for de truth and look out for dose Bush—look out for dose Bush, dey is hell." Niles adds: "The storyteller thought the so-called Boche [French slang for Germans], mispronounced 'Bush,' were an entirely different army."

MISTER FRENCH RAILROAD MAN

Oh, you joined up for fight-in' in a he-man's war, __ And you're goin' to do your fight-in' in a French freight car. __ Oh, mis-ter French rail-road man, _____ where you tak-in' us to? _____

50

Ride all night and ride all day—
Got to stand up straight 'cause there's no place to lay.   *Chorus*

Forty men and eight army horses—
Goin' to come back home with some nice German crosses.   *Chorus*

If I get home to the land of the free,
Pullman train'll be the place for me.   *Chorus*

Mister Engineer, won't you please haul your freight,
My feet is singin' a hymn of hate.   *Chorus*

Oh, I know there's trouble up yonder ahead,
But it wouldn't much matter if I could lay my head.   *Chorus*

A black battalion lays a railroad track in France during World War I. At the time most black troops were used as work crews rather than as combat soldiers.

This is another soldier's song from World War I. The involvement of the United States in World War I caused a quandary for African Americans, who were hesitant to serve in the army of a country that denied them basic civil rights. Many black men, however, felt it was their patriotic duty to enlist. Due to racist policies within the army, most black troops were assigned to support details—tasks such as kitchen work, supply duties, and the eternal diggin'.

DIGGIN'

Dig-gin', dig-gin', dig-gin' in Ken-tuck-y, Dig-gin' in ___ Ten-nes-see,

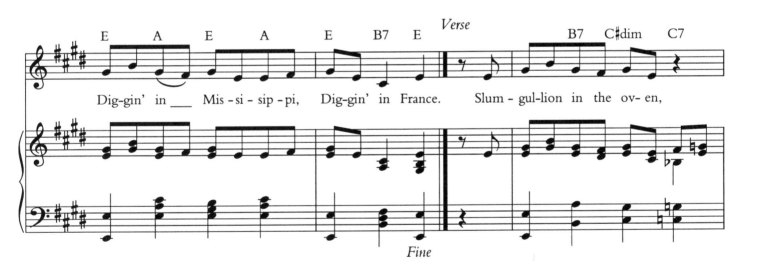

Dig-gin' in ___ Mis-si-sip-pi, Dig-gin' in France. Slum-gul-lion in the ov-en,

Cof-fee in the pot. Snap your-self up in-to line, An' get it while it's hot.

Sharpen up my shovel,
And shine up my pick,
'Cause I can't scratch this hard cold ground
With a crooked stick.   *Chorus*

Motor trucks and caissons
Cut a mighty trench.
Have to pile the metal on
For these poor damn French.   *Chorus*

This song comes to us by way of an old, scratchy recording made by bluesman Blind Lemon Jefferson in 1928. Jefferson was a street singer who sang the blues throughout his home country of the Southwest, sometimes performing as far north as Chicago. He recorded many of his songs, including "Lonesome House Blues," for the Paramount Recording Company in Chicago, which sold so-called race records in Chicago and throughout the South.

LONESOME HOUSE BLUES

I'm goin' away, momma, just to wear you off my mind.
I'm goin' away, pretty momma, just to wear you off my mind.
If I live here in Chicago, money's gonna be my crime.

My house is lonesome, my baby left me all alone.
This house is lonesome— she left me all alone.
If your heart ain't rock, sugar, it must be marble stone.

I got the blues so bad, it hurts my feet to walk.
I got the blues so bad, it hurts my feet to walk.
It has settled on my brain, and it hurts my tongue to talk.

This woman's ballad contains lines reminiscent of "Careless Love" and "I Know You, Rider." Many traditional songs use phrases, musical snatches, and ideas from other songs. The original folk singers, singing for their own entertainment and unconcerned with recording contracts or copyright laws, felt free to borrow melodies and lyrics and reshape them to suit their own needs.

FARE THEE WELL

If I had wings like Noah's dove, I'd fly up the river to the man I love.

Fare thee well, oh, honey, Fare thee well.

I've got a man and he's long and tall.
Moves his body like a cannon ball.
Fare thee well, O honey, fare thee well.

'Member one night, a-drizzlin' rain,
Round my heart I felt a pain.
Fare thee well, O honey, fare thee well.

When I wore my apron low,
Couldn't keep you from my do'.
Fare thee well, O honey, fare thee well.

Now I wear my apron high,
Scarcely ever see you passing by.
Fare thee well, O honey, fare thee well.

Now my apron's up to my chin,
You pass my door and you won't come in
Fare thee well, O honey, fare thee well.

If had listened to what my mama said,
I'd be at home in my mama's bed.
Fare thee well, O honey, fare thee well.

One of these days, and it won't be long,
Call my name and I'll be gone.
Fare thee well, O honey, fare thee well.

"In the Pines" is what traditional singers call a "big ballad." It tells a long, powerful, dramatic, and ultimately tragic story. But although "In the Pines" is undeniably somber in tone, it does not have a single consistent story. Instead, it tells a number of seemingly unrelated, interwoven tales. Each tale picks up a mournful thread from the preceding verse. Although the listener may not be sure where the song is headed, it is a chilly tune nonetheless.

In the Pines

True ___ love, true love, don't ___
slept in the pines, Where the

lie to me, ___ Tell me where did you sleep last
sun nev-er shines, ___ and I shiv ered with cold and

night? _____ I ___ ___
fright. _____

Tell me, where did you get them pretty little shoes
And the dress you wear so fine?
I got my shoes from a railroad man,
Got my dress from a driver in the mine.

I wish to the Lord I'd-a never been born,
Or died when I was young.
I never would have kissed your sweet, sweet lips,
Nor heard your rattling tongue.

59

The longest train I ever did ride
Was a hundred coaches long.
The only woman I ever did love,
She's on that train and gone.

Them long steel rails and them short crossties
Ain't got no end I know.
On these long steel rails and short crossties
I'm tramping my way back home.

Longest old train in this whole wide world
Comes around Joe Brown's coal mine.
Headlight comes 'round when the sun come up,
The caboose when the sun goes down.

Yes, my husband was a railroad man,
Was the best in this high lonesome world.
The only thing that he did that was wrong
Was to miss just a-one little curve.

My husband was a railroad man—
Killed a mile and a half from town.
I found his head in an engine wheel
But his body could never be found.

True love, true love, tell me where will you go?
I'm gonna go where the cold winds blow.
I'm gonna weep, gonna cry, gonna moan, gonna sigh,
Gonna dance in my good-time clothes.

Despite all of the heartbreak and riders in ballads, there are songs like this one that tell of real love, understanding, support, and compassion. This song was orginally recorded by blues great Tampa Red in 1941, and it has since been recorded by such luminaries as Big Bill Broonzy, Elmore James, and Junior Wells.

WHEN THINGS GO WRONG WITH YOU

I love you, ba-by, ___ I ain't gon' lie, ___ With-out you,

ba-by, ___ I just can't be sat-is-fied. ___ 'Cause when things go

wrong, ___ so wrong with you, ___ it hurts me too. ___

So, run here.

So, run here, baby,
Put your little hands in mine,
I've got something to tell you, baby,
I know, that will change your mind.   *Chorus*

I want you, baby,
Just to understand,
I don't want to be your boss, baby,
I just want to be your man.   *Chorus*

Now, when you go home,
You don't get along,
Come back to me, baby,
Where I live, that's your home.   *Chorus*

I love you, baby,
You know it's true,
I wouldn't mistreat you, baby,
Not for nothing in this world like you.   *Chorus*

Jerry Silverman is one of America's most prolific authors of music books. He has a B.S. degree in music from the City College of New York and an M.A. in musicology from New York University. He has authored some 100 books dealing with various aspects of guitar, banjo, violin, and fiddle technique, as well as numerous songbooks and arrangements for other instruments. He teaches guitar and music to children and adults and performs in folk-song concerts before audiences of all ages.

Kenneth B. Clark received a Ph.D. in social psychology from Columbia University and is the author of numerous books and articles on race and education. His books include *Prejudice and Your Child*, *Dark Ghetto*, and *Pathos of Power*. Long noted as an authority on segregation in schools, his work was cited by the U.S. Supreme Court in its decision in the historic *Brown v. Board of Education of Topeka* case in 1954. Dr. Clark, Distinguished Professor of Psychology Emeritus at the City University of New York, is the president of Kenneth B. Clark & Associates, a consulting firm specializing in personnel matters, race relations, and affirmative action programs.